Toddler Tales

Illustrated by Katie Saunders

Archie the Fireman

Archie wanted to be a fireman. He loved wearing his big fireman's hat. Sometimes he pretended he was climbing a fireman's tall ladder.

But Archie wanted to be a REAL fireman. He wanted to show how brave he was.

"You can't be a real fireman," Amy giggled. "You're far too little, Archie!"

There was a knock at the door. It was Amy's friend Sasha. She wanted to show the Toddler Twins her new kitten.

"She's so fluffy!" cried Amy.

"She's very small, she gets scared," Sasha said passing the kitten to Amy.

But the little kitten wasn't scared of Amy at all. She just purred softly.

"Do you want to stroke her, Archie?" Sasha asked kindly.

Archie wasn't listening.

So Amy gently passed the kitten back to Sasha. But the tiny kitten suddenly leapt out of Sasha's arms.

She ran around the house and into the back garden. Amy, Archie and Sasha all followed quickly.

"Oh no!" cried Sasha. "She's never climbed a tree before. She'll get stuck!"

And that's just what happened. The kitten didn't know how to climb down the tree again.

"How are we going to get her down?" cried Amy. "She's too scared to jump," added Sasha tearfully.

Archie jumped into action. He ran back into the house to fetch his fireman's helmet. Then he raced across the garden to the slide. Clever Archie had an idea!

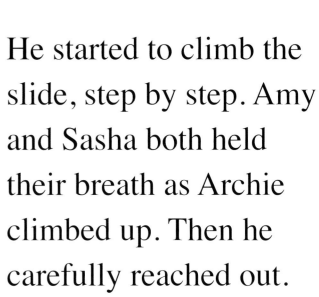

He started to climb the slide, step by step. Amy and Sasha both held their breath as Archie climbed up. Then he carefully reached out.

Soon the frightened kitten was safely in his hands!

"Oh, brave Archie!" Amy clapped joyfully.

He carried the kitten carefully. It was like a fireman's ladder. "I knew I could be a real fireman," called Archie as Amy and Sasha cheered loudly.

The Lost Pets

Archie and Amy searched everywhere for their three pets. But they couldn't find the dog, the cat or even the rabbit. Suddenly Amy ran back to the house.

"Where are you going?" called Archie.

"You'll see!" Amy giggled.

When she came back, she carried a bone in one hand and a saucer of milk in the other hand. And she had a carrot under her arm.

"These will help us find them!" she giggled again. Amy then put the saucer of milk in the middle of the garden. Soon there was a rustling in the bushes. One of their pets was starting to creep out of its hiding place. Who do you think it was?

It was the cat! She loved milk. She ran out of the bushes, straight to the saucer. Just as she was licking her whiskers, Amy chuckled, "Got you!" And she gave her a big cuddle.

Next, Amy put the big carrot in the middle of the garden. Very soon, they heard rustling in the bushes.

"Who do you think it is?" Amy whispered.

"I know!" whispered Archie.

And out of the bushes hopped a fluffy bunny. As he nibbled the carrot, Archie pounced.

"Got you!" Archie giggled, lifting him up. He was careful not the drop the carrot too!

And just at that moment, the dog ran out of the bushes.

"He must have smelt the bone!" cried Archie. The dog wagged his tail and chewed happily on the bone.

"You're so clever, Amy," Archie said as they now led their pets back into the house.

"Yes," laughed Amy. "I know what to do next time you hide from me, Archie. I'll put your favourite sweets in the middle of the garden!"

Nurse Amy

Amy loved playing "Doctors and Nurses". Sometimes she was the doctor but today she was the nurse. And she was very busy. Teddy's head was too hot, so she tucked him in bed.

Giraffe hurt his neck, so she wrapped a bandage around it.

But Archie wanted Amy to play with him.

"Let's go to the park," he said. "I'll push you on the swings if you want."

Amy shook her head.

So Archie wandered into the garden. He kicked a ball …

he climbed a tree …

… he found a really good hiding place. But it wasn't much fun without Amy.

Archie went inside to play with his toy robot. He pressed a button and made the robot walk. Suddenly, the robot walked right off the table and fell on the floor.

He picked it up but the robot wouldn't work any more. Archie was now sadder than ever.

"It's broken!" he told Amy, trying not to cry as he showed her the robot.

"Let's see if we can make him better," Amy told Archie kindly in her best "nurse" voice.

"You can be the doctor," she added. She held the robot's hand so that he wouldn't be scared.

First Archie checked the robot's arms. Then he gently moved its legs backwards and forwards. He stood the robot on the table. It started walking again!

"What a clever doctor you are, Archie," said Amy.

"And what a kind nurse you are," Archie replied.
"Let's find some more toys to make better," cried Archie.

And they spent the rest
of the day looking after
all the sick toys.

The Wet Park

Amy and Archie waited all morning for the rain to stop. Then they set off for the park and took some sandwiches for lunch. But when they arrived, the climbing frame was wet. And so was the roundabout.

Archie thought the slide looked dry. But the raindrops had made a little puddle at the bottom of the slide. Archie whooshed right through it!

"Poor Archie!" said Amy, trying not to giggle. But it was soon Amy's turn to get wet as she sat on the swing. The twins then checked the sandpit, the see-saw and the wobbly logs. They were all still wet. But then they both spotted something.

The duck pond! They had great fun sharing their sandwiches with the ducks. This was the one place in the park where it really did not matter being wet!

The Beach Race

Amy and Archie ran on to the beach. Archie couldn't wait to start building a sandcastle. And Amy wanted to find some crabs.

"Let's have a race!" said Archie. "See if I can build a big castle before you can find a crab!"

Amy loved having races so hurried off towards the rocks. She needed to find a crab quickly. Archie was already digging.

She was lucky! She spotted a crab sitting at the bottom of a pool. She gently fished it out and put it in her bucket. She was sure she was going to win the race now.

But suddenly Amy knocked the bucket and the crab scampered away. She looked everywhere but the crab was nowhere to be seen.

Amy was very upset. She could see that Archie had nearly finished his castle. So she sadly put her fishing net over her shoulder. She wandered slowly back to Archie.

When she reached him, he was just adding a flag to the top of his castle. He had finished!

"I thought you were going to win our race," he cried excitedly. "But I just finished in time. So, we both won!"

Amy did not understand what Archie meant.

But then Amy noticed Archie looking at her fishing net. Turning her head, she saw a little crab clinging on to the net. So Archie was right. They did both win!

The Treasure Hunt

Amy had lost her toy rabbit, Pinky.

"Let's have a treasure hunt!" cried Archie. He loved treasure hunts.

"Not now," said Amy, almost crying.

Toys

"I'll look for Pinky in the garden," said Archie brightly.

Archie searched under the swing, under the slide and under the little tree where Amy always had picnics with Pinky.

Amy was still looking for Pinky when Archie ran in.

"I've made you a treasure hunt," he cried. "I'll help you look for Pinky when you've found the treasure."

So Amy started looking in the garden.

She wanted to find the treasure quickly so they could look for Pinky again.

"I've hidden the treasure in something red," Archie said excitedly.

"I know!" she said running towards the red flowers. But the treasure wasn't there. Then she found a little red bucket in the sandpit.

Amy quickly
picked it up.

"Look inside!"
shouted Archie.

And there
was Pinky!

"I found her under the
tree," Archie giggled.
"Then I hid her again
to give you the best
treasure hunt ever!"

Amy gave Pinky a big
hug. Then she gave
Archie a big hug as well.

Picnic Shopping

The Toddler Twins were shopping for their picnic.

"What shall we buy?" Amy asked as they pushed the trolley around the shop.

"Jelly!" cried Archie.

"We need cheese and ham for our sandwiches," said Amy. Then they picked up apples, grapes and some drinks. Amy also chose two iced cakes. "Just right for a picnic," she smiled.

And Amy felt very clever that she remembered the paper napkins and spoons. But Archie was worried that they had forgotten something. What could it be? They had cheese and ham for sandwiches and jelly and fruit.

Suddenly they remembered the most important thing of all. You can't make sandwiches without – BREAD! They had to push their trolley around the shop again. It was lucky that they both liked shopping!

Farm Twins

The Toddler Twins Amy and Archie were very
excited. Farmer George was driving them around
his farm in a tractor. It was a very bumpy ride!
First, they stopped to see the pigs.

"Those baby pigs are just like you two!" George told the twins.

"But we don't have pink faces and squashed noses," said Archie.

"And we don't like playing in the mud," said Amy. "Well … only Archie does."

Farmer George chuckled. "They're just like you two because they're brother and sister and were born at the same time. They're TWINS."

Next, Farmer George took Archie and Amy to see his goats. There were two baby goats playing with their mother.

"Those baby goats are just like you two!" George told the twins.

"Does that mean we'll grow horns?" asked Archie, rather worried.

"And a beard?" asked Amy.

"No!" the farmer chuckled. "They're like you because they're brother and sister and were born at the same time. They're TWINS."

"Would you like to see some more animals?" Farmer George asked.

"Yes please!" cried the twins and they raced back to the tractor.

So Farmer George took Archie and Amy to see his sheep. There were two cute lambs running and jumping around their mother.

"Those baby lambs are just like you two!" George told the twins. This time Archie and Amy knew exactly what George meant.

The two lambs were just like them. Not because Archie had a fluffy face or Amy had a white tail. The lambs were TWINS … just like the two baby pigs and just like the two baby goats. And just like Archie and Amy!

The Snowman

One morning the garden was covered in snow when Amy and Archie woke up.

"Let's build a snowman!" cried Archie. He wanted to run out straightaway.

"You'll freeze in your pyjamas!" laughed Amy.

So the twins started to look for warm clothes. First, Archie took out a white floppy hat.

"That's a sun hat!" giggled Amy.

Archie found a woolly hat just right for a snowy day. And then he spotted his pom-pom hat.

Amy picked up her favourite sandals.

"Your toes will get wet!" Archie told her. So Amy went to find a pair of wellies instead.

"Will this be okay?" asked Archie, as he pulled out a large stripy jumper.

"Perfect!" replied Amy, poking her head through a woolly jumper.

"And a scarf?" asked Archie. He took two out of the drawer.

"Good idea! And some gloves," said Amy.

As they ran into the garden, Amy and Archie screamed with delight. They started with a very small snowball and rolled it in the thick snow.

"Wow!" cried Archie as the snowball grew bigger and bigger.

Then they made a smaller one for the snowman's head. They carefully lifted the head on top of the body.

Amy ran into the kitchen for a carrot for the snowman's nose and currants for his eyes. Archie found some twigs for his arms.

"He doesn't look finished," said Amy sadly.

"I know!" cried Archie. And he took off one of his scarves and his pom-pom hat.

"Much better!" laughed Amy. "Now the snowman is warm like us!"

The Pirates

Amy and Archie always took their favourite toys to nursery. Archie liked to carry his toy car. Amy kept Pinky, her toy rabbit, in her hand. But today they needed both arms free to play dressing up.

They decided to dress up as pirates. First, they put on some baggy trousers and big shiny boots. Then they put on a large belt and tucked in a toy sword.

Next they fixed a black patch over one eye. And they finished by putting on a big pirate hat.

Now they both looked just like real pirates. The problem was that their nursery teacher was unable to tell them apart. You could not see their hair tucked under their hats.

She needed to hear them speak. Then she could tell who was Amy and who was Archie.

"What wonderful pirates you both look!" the teacher told them kindly. "Who's the fiercest pirate?"

The Toddler Twins thought it would be funny not to say anything. So, Amy just pointed at Archie to show that he was the fiercest pirate!

The teacher realised that the twins were playing a game.
She tried to think of another way of telling them apart.
She suddenly spotted their favourite toys.

"Don't forget your toy car and rabbit," she told them.

The Toddler Twins immediately picked up their favourite toys. "Now I know," their teacher chuckled.

"You're Amy holding the toy rabbit! And you're Archie holding the toy car!" And she was right!

Toddler Quiz

1. What did Nurse Amy wrap around giraffe's neck?

2. Can you remember which animals have horns and a beard?

3. Amy found this on the beach

4. Which pet ate the carrot?

5. Amy and Archie would not put this in their sandwich

6. What did Archie hide as the treasure?

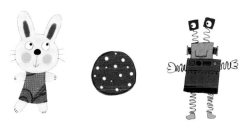

7. How many ducks did the twins see in the pond?

8. Archie did not wear these in the snow

9. Which hat did the Pirate Twins wear?

10. Who did Fireman Archie rescue in the tree?